New Shoes

written by Jay Dale

illustrated by Anthea Whitworth

"Here is a shoe shop,"
said Mum.
"Come inside with me.
You can get
new shoes today."

3

Tim looked down
at his red shoes.
"No," cried Tim.
"I like my red shoes."

"Your red shoes
are too little," said Mum.
"Come inside the shoe shop
with me."

"Look at the big blue shoes,"
said Mum.
"They will fit you."

Tim did not look
at the blue shoes.
He looked
down at his red shoes.
"I like my red shoes,"
cried Tim.

"Come on, Tim," said Mum.
"The blue shoes
will look good on you."

Tim went up and down
in the blue shoes.

"Mum," said Tim.
"The blue shoes
look good on me.
Can I get new shoes today?"

15

"Yes," said Mum.
"You can get
the big blue shoes.
They look good on you!"